E
IG
S!
tterland
uniqu



This book belon

James Mew
doe

# Useful words

(in the order they appear in this book)

hat

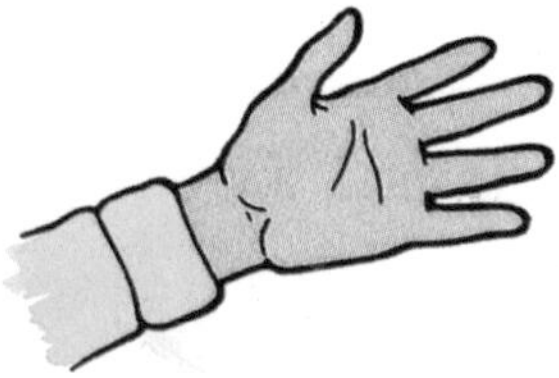

hand

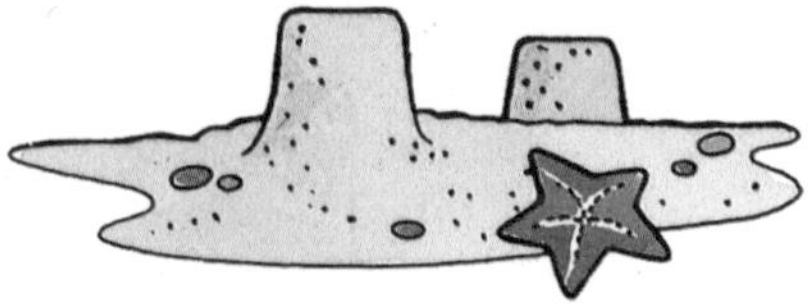

sand

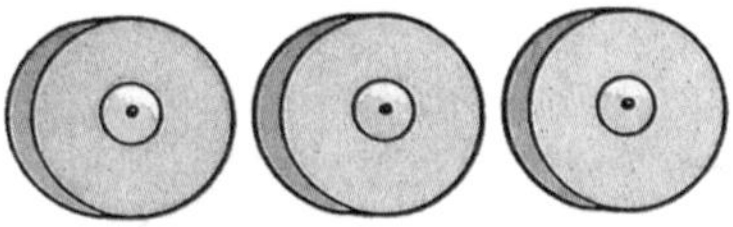

wheels

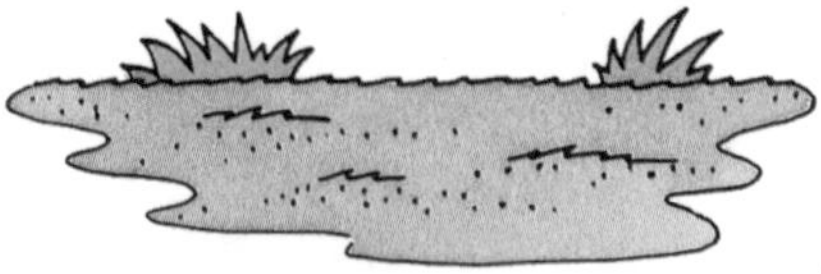

ground

balls

petals

flowers

flags

towers

puppies

park

zebras

apples

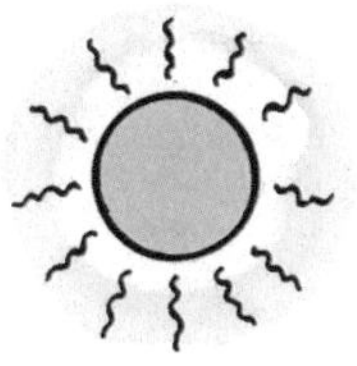

sun

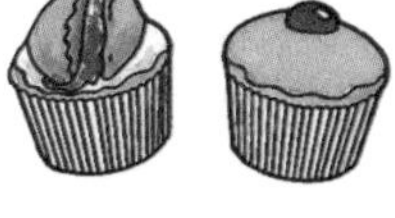

cakes

# Ten cakes!

Maire Buonocore

# 1

# one

One hat in his hand ...

# 2

# two

Two snakes in the sand.

# 3

# three

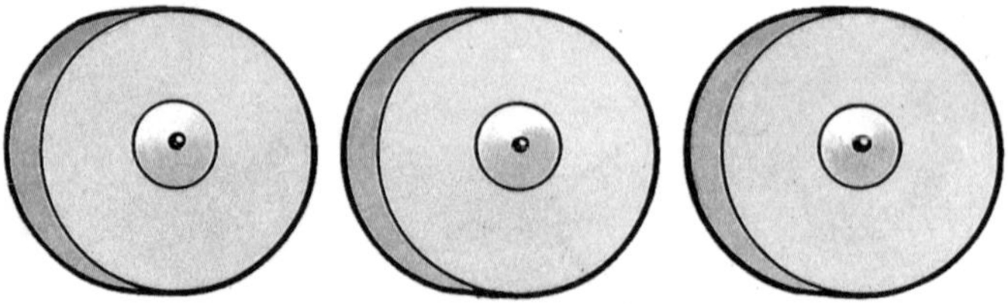

Three wheels on the ground ...

# 4

# four

Four balls going round.

# 5

# five

Five petals on the flowers ...

# 6

# six

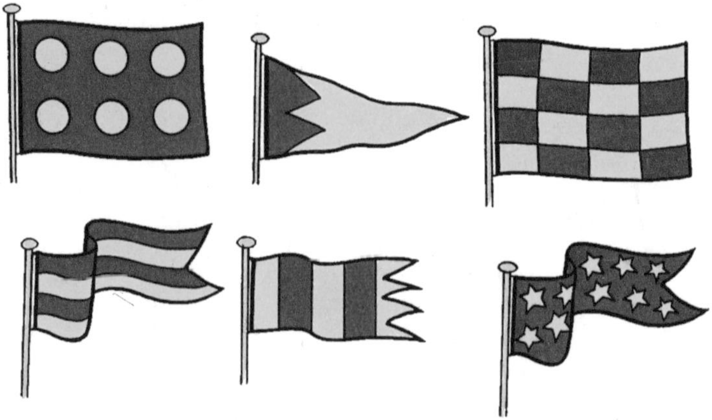

Six flags on the towers.

# 7

# seven

Seven puppies in the park ...

# 8

# eight

Eight zebras in the dark.

# 9

# nine

Nine apples in the sun ...

# 10

# ten

Ten cakes ...

Let's all have one!

# Ten cakes

One hat in his hand,

Two snakes in the sand.

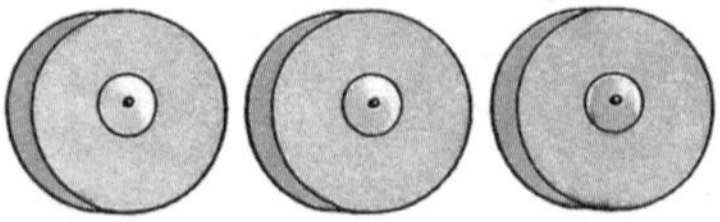

Three wheels on the ground,

Four balls going round.

Five petals on the flowers,

Six flags on the towers.

Seven puppies in the park,

Eight zebras in the dark.

Nine apples in the sun,

Ten cakes ... Let's all have one!

# The Letterlanders

Annie Apple | Bouncy Ben | Clever Cat | Dippy Duck | Eddy Elephant | Fireman Fred | Golden Girl

Hairy Hat Man | Impy Ink | Jumping Jim | Kicking King | Lucy Lamp Lady | Munching Mike

Naughty Nick | Oscar Orange | Poor Peter | Quarrelsome Queen | Robber Red | Sammy Snake | Ticking Tess

Uppy Umbrella | Vase of Violets | Wicked Water Witch | Max and Maxine | Yo-yo Man | Zig Zag Zebra

Published by Collins Educational
An imprint of HarperCollins*Publishers* Ltd
77-85 Fulham Palace Road
London W6 8JB



First published 1998

ISBN 0 00 303376 7



British Library Cataloguing in Publication Data
A catalogue record for this book is available from the British Library.

Written by Maire Buonocore
Illustrated by Anna Jupp and Jan West
Colouring by Gina Hart
Designed by Michael Sturley
Consultant: Lyn Wendon, originator of Letterland

Printed by Printing Express, Hong Kong